Developing History

UNDERSTANDING AND INTERPRETING THE PAST

Ages 7-8

Rhona Whiteford

A & C BLACK

Contents

Published 2007 by A & C Black Publishers Limited
38 Soho Square, London W1D 3HB
www.acblack.com

ISBN 978-0-7136-8393-6

Copyright text and illustrations © Bender Richardson White
Copyright cover illustration © Sholto Walker
Project managers: Lionel Bender and Ben White
Editors: Lucy Poddington and Deborah Kespert
Design: Susan McIntyre
Illustrator: Jon Mitchell

The publishers would like to thank Rick Weights and Alf Wilkinson of the Historical Association for their advice.

A CIP catalogue record for this book is available from the British Library.

Printed in Great Britain by Martins the Printers.

This book is produced using paper that is made from wood grown in managed, sustainable forests. It is natural, renewable and recyclable. The logging and manufacturing processes conform to the environmental regulations of the country of origin.

Introduction

Developing History is a series of seven photocopiable activity books for history lessons. Each book provides a range of activities that not only develop children's knowledge and understanding of events, people and changes in the past, but also provide opportunities to develop their investigative and interpretive skills.

The activities vary in their approach. Some are based on first-hand observations, some present text and images for the children to analyse, and others require the children to find information from books and electronic sources. They focus on questioning, observing, generating thoughts and ideas, planning, carrying out investigations, recording findings, checking and questioning findings, and presenting explanations. The activities include independent and group work.

The activities in **Developing History: Ages 7–8** are based on the QCA schemes of work for history at Key Stage 1 and support children's development in the following areas from the programme of study:
- place events and objects in chronological order
- use common words and phrases relating to the passing of time
- recognise why people did things, why events happened and what happened as a result
- identify differences between ways of life at different times
- identify different ways in which the past is represented
- find out about the past from a range of sources of information
- ask and answer questions about the past
- communicate in a variety of ways.

The activities are linked with other areas of the curriculum where appropriate.

Each activity specifies the learning outcome and features a **Teachers' note** at the foot of the page, which may be masked before photocopying. This will flag any resources needed for the activity. Expanded teaching notes are also provided in the **Notes on the activities** on pages 5–11. This section gives further information and provides key vocabulary to work through at the start of each activity.

Most of the activity sheets end with a challenge (**Now try this!**) which reinforces and extends the children's learning and provides the teacher with an opportunity for assessment. These activities might be appropriate for only a few children; it is not expected that the whole class should complete them. A separate sheet of paper will be needed for some of the extension activities.

Most children will be able to carry out the activities independently. It is not expected that the children will be able to read all the instructions on the sheets, but that someone will read with them. Children gradually become accustomed to seeing instructions, and learn their purpose long before they can read them.

Organisation and resources

Most activities require few resources beyond pencils and general classroom items, including spare paper on occasion. To give all children the best opportunity for developing effectively their knowledge and understanding of the world the children will need opportunities to gather information and satisfy their curiosity. They will begin to understand the past by examining appropriate artefacts (such as toys played with by their parents when they were young), looking at books, using CD-ROMs, audio and visual reference material, pictures, photographs, maps and by talking to visitors and making visits. Consequently, there will be times when children will need additional resources to complete the activities. These will be pointed out in the **Teachers' note**. It would also be useful to have a chart on the wall listing the days and months.

You may want to use interactive whiteboards or overhead projectors to display the activity sheets or source materials. You will also find it helpful to build up your own resource bank of books, posters, newspapers and old photographs, especially of your local area or historic sites you and your class could visit.

Structure of a history lesson

To get the best use of the activity sheets, gather all the resources you need before the lesson. Spend 10–15 minutes discussing the activity and making sure all the children understand what they have to do and how they will achieve it. Give the children about 20 minutes on the activity. Allow 5–10 minutes for whole-class review and consolidation at the end.

Useful websites

You can find information and pictures relating to the topics in this book on the following websites:

www.victorianweb.org

www.buildingsoflondon.co.uk

www.britishlegion.org.uk

www.britishmuseum.org

www.bbc.co.uk/history/forkids

Notes on the activities

The notes below expand upon those provided at the foot of the activity pages. They give ideas for making the most of the activity sheet, including suggestions for the whole-class introduction and discussion or for follow-up work using an adapted version of the sheet. To help teachers to select appropriate learning experiences for their pupils, the activities are grouped into sections, but the pages need not be presented in the order in which they appear unless stated otherwise.

Why have people invaded and settled in Britain in the past?

The following four activities can be used in conjunction with any work on invaders and settlers. They focus on developing an initial understanding of the concepts of invasion and settlement. Ask the children if they can name any peoples from the past or present who have come to Britain either aggressively as invaders or as settlers to join our society. This discussion can be linked to work in citizenship about immigration and prejudice.

Moving (page 12) aims to help the children understand that there are different reasons why people move from the place where they were born, that some people choose to leave and others are forced. You could show short video clips or stills of different modern people moving home, including refugees in other countries and people affected by natural disasters. Discuss the reasons why they are moving. Make a chart together to show local or national ethnic diversity in modern Britain. In an unmixed community, refer to television soaps as a source of information. Use a world map to locate the ethnic origin of different peoples. This can be linked with work in geography (Investigating our local area and connecting ourselves to the world).

> **Vocabulary:** *travel, removal, rebuild, settle.*

Coming to Britain (page 13) helps the children recognise that people have always moved between different areas. To introduce the invaders or settlers you are studying, add the relevant period to the class timeline and discuss events the children know of before and after, to put it in context. Show pictures of the invaders or settlers and discuss how the people living in Britain may have reacted to their arrival. To develop their understanding of how both sides felt, the children can work in pairs to produce a short news interview with one child as interviewer and the other as witness or expert. The interviewer can ask the questions on the activity sheet for the other to answer. Ask the class to assess the performance. This links with work in literacy (Speaking and listening).

> **Vocabulary:** *travel, settle, origin, emigrate, immigrant.*

Invaders and settlers: 1 and **2** (pages 14–15) shows who settled in Britain a long time ago. First identify all our main early invaders and their homelands. Discuss reasons for their fairly local journeys. Brainstorm a list of all possible modern forms of transport, then speculate about which were available to the invaders you are studying. In groups, the children could generate ideas about where the travellers might have got food and shelter on the journey and discuss what it would have been like to eat and sleep in an open boat.

> **Vocabulary:** *homeland, journey, transport, travellers.*

Take a good look (page 16) shows what can be learned from archaeological remains. Explain that artefacts are man-made objects and can be classified by use: machine, tool, vehicle, ornament, toy. Encourage very careful examination of the artefact to infer something of the user's lifestyle. With real artefacts (and reproductions – but make sure children know the difference) ask the children to draw the object from several angles to encourage more acute observation. This can link with their work on first-hand observation in art. Link also to ICT and use digital photography to record all aspects, including a comparative measurement such as a ruler or a hand. Explain that artefacts are evidence of the culture, the technology and the environment. This activity can also be linked with work in science (Characteristics of materials).

> **Vocabulary:** *artefact, material, examine.*

A Roman case study

People of Britain and Rome (page 17) compares the lifestyles, homelands, appearance and dress of Celts and Romans. Show the children photographs of Britain's and Italy's landscapes from websites such as www.corbis.com. Make inferences about the countries' climates and discuss reasons for the clothes of these peoples to be different. For background information, websites www.bbc.co.uk/schools/romans and www.bbc.co.uk/wales/celts (Fact File) will also be useful. Help the children discover why the Romans wanted to come here, how long they stayed and how they adapted to the climate. You could use evidence such as statues and murals to show different kinds of Roman dress and ask the children to paint or draw Roman people of different ages and professions. Mount with the children's own explanatory labels and captions.

> **Vocabulary:** *lifestyle, wealthy, material, weapon, jewellery.*

A Roman soldier's pack (page 18) helps the children select and record information about the Roman way of life. A legionary's campaign pack enabled each man to feed, water and protect himself: it included weapons, blankets and a spade to dig latrines and ramparts for defence. Compare with modern army gear. Discuss the idea of invasion by an enemy army and what evidence archaeologists have found of the Romans in Britain. You could use photographs from the website blog.arlt.co.uk/blog/ErmineStreetGuard to show replica dress, armour and machinery of war. Dramatic footage of armies could also be shown from the film *Gladiator* or the BBC series *Rome*. Look at a map of Europe to see the distances marched by the conquering Roman armies.

> **Vocabulary:** *legionary, campaign, journey, equipment.*

Latin phrasebook (page 19) shows the impact and legacy of the Romans in Britain. Encourage the children to research evidence of Roman writing in Britain: tombstones, inscriptions on artefacts and buildings, coins, books, maps and scrolls. Display photographs or drawings of such evidence, add captions and match them to the site where they were found on a map of Britain. (See the British Museum and Hadrian's Wall websites.) Make a list together of modern and Roman uses of writing. Many languages were used in Rome but Latin was used for all official discourse and writing.

> **Vocabulary:** *language, Latin, numerals, inscription, scroll.*

Boudicca's revolt (page 20) focuses on the main events in and reasons for Boudicca's revolt. Use a variety of sources for the story: books, modern works of art, photographs of statues of Boudicca, and websites. You could read extracts from Rosemary Sutcliff's *Song for a Dark Queen* (1978) and short written extracts about Boudicca from contemporary writers like Tacitus and Cassius Dio. Make lists of reasons for the revolt and what happened afterwards. On a map of Britain, the children can mark the places of importance in Boudicca's revolt: the modern East Anglian area, London, Colchester and St Albans. Discuss the children's possible reactions to other children invading their garden or play area and link this to citizenship discussions about what is fair and not fair.

> **Vocabulary:** *revolt, rebel, rebellion, tribe, hill fort, defend, chariot.*

Visit to a Roman town (page 21) compares Roman and Celtic lifestyles. To prepare for the activity you could show the children suitable extracts from the BBC series *Rome* which include reconstructions of amphitheatres, markets, homes and streets. Also review their work on clothes and perhaps have a Roman meal with fruits and vegetables, bread and soft drinks for wine and beer. As a follow-up activity, ask small groups to devise play scenes of different aspects of Roman life: the town crier's news, a sale at a market stall, someone buying medicines. Ask them to include Celts in the scenes. This links with literacy (Speaking and listening).

> **Vocabulary:** *forum, amphitheatre, market, baths, barracks, temple.*

An Anglo-Saxon case study

Jumbled up Anglo-Saxons (page 22) helps the children to recognise characteristics of Anglo-Saxon dress. Provide a selection of books and pictures for the children to look at. They could also explore suitable websites. Discuss their ideas about the sources, style, practicality, status and decoration of clothes. Collect photographs of accessories such as jewellery, belts and girdles, and help the children to identify the materials used and infer reasons for fabrics rarely surviving. You could show pictures of artefacts that indicate that the Anglo-Saxons made textiles: loom frames, loom weights, needles, remains of fabric. Help the children work out how they were used. Clothes were hard to make and expensive and so they were indicators of wealth and status.

> **Vocabulary:** *tunic, cloak, headdress, material, loom.*

Skilful Anglo-Saxons (page 23) focuses on the way of life of the Anglo-Saxons. Explain that the Anglo-Saxons lived in self-sufficient village communities and grew, hunted, collected and made whatever they needed, trading only for luxuries. Skills were so varied that there must have been specialist craftspeople; point out examples of artefacts such as the Sutton Hoo helmet, the illuminated Lindisfarne Gospels, fine brooches, churches, jewelled crosses and textile art such as knitted socks and embroidery. The Anglo-Saxons mined, smelted and crafted all metals and minted coins for trade. There is little evidence that they had machines, but they must have grown a wide range of crops. Link this with work in science (Helping plants grow well).

> **Vocabulary:** *natural resources, artefacts, evidence.*

The ship burial at Sutton Hoo (page 24) helps the children to make inferences about archaeological evidence. Historians think the Sutton Hoo ship grave is that of the Anglo-Saxon king Raedwald. Discuss why no human remains were found and remind the children that physical finds tell only part of a story. Body salts present show a body was there but decomposed. Ask the children to make detailed observations and drawings of the artefacts from photographs on website: www.archaeology.co.uk/ca/timeline/saxon/suttonhoo/ suttonhoo.htm.

You could do a large class painting of the ship burial with children's captions describing each of the grave goods.

> **Vocabulary:** *archaeology, artefacts, site, excavate, burial.*

Anglo-Saxon health quiz (page 25) is designed to encourage the children find out about the way of life of the Anglo-Saxons using several sources. Evidence in bones, rubbish tips and cesspits shows poor health, amputations, breaks and arthritis. Show children how to extract information from sources, making notes and quick drawings for reference. List the resources and conditions we have to keep healthy (hospitals, clean water, toilets, medicines, fresh foods, rubbish collection, dental checks, exercise, sleep) and contrast this with a list of Anglo-Saxon health measures. Magic charms were written in the runic script to ward off illness and evil. Link this activity with work in science (Teeth and eating).

> **Vocabulary:** *medicine, health, cesspit, indigestion, diarrhoea, amputation, arthritis.*

The Battle of Hastings (page 26) helps the children to place the Anglo-Saxon and Viking periods in a chronological framework and looks at ideas related to settlement and invasion. Tell the children that the Bayeux Tapestry is in fact an embroidery (stitched rather than woven) and shows pictures of many aspects of Norman lifestyle, as well as the events of the Battle of Hastings. Remind them that the population of England at the time of the battle was a mix of Anglo-Saxons and Vikings. Discuss the idea of a pictorial record like the tapestry and explain this was because few people could read. Explain that nothing is known for certain about the origin of the tapestry, but it was probably made in the 1070s for Bishop Odo of Bayeux, the half-brother of William the Conqueror. As a follow-up activity you could provide key pictures from the tapestry (see www.bayeuxtapestry.org.uk) for groups of children to make detailed copies and to write commentary and imagined speech bubbles for the scenes. Link this with literacy and ask the children to write different accounts (letter, news report or story) of the events.

> **Vocabulary:** *battle, Hastings, Bayeux Tapestry, Norman, conquest, William the Conqueror, invade, settle.*

A Viking case study

Viking raiders (page 27) encourages the children to make inferences about the Viking way of life, and to recognise characteristics that place Vikings a long time ago in the past. Mark the class timeline with the first Viking raid by Norwegian Vikings at Lindisfarne in AD 793. Discuss why ships were needed, why they were different shapes and sizes, how they were built, how the Vikings found other lands, why they wanted to travel and what they needed for the journey. Talk about why a compass, phone, first-aid kit and maps were not available to the Vikings. Using photographs, identify characteristics of the Viking homelands in Scandinavia and locate the countries on a world map or globe. Note their proximity to Britain and other lands they invaded. It will be helpful also to show photographs of people in re-enactment groups wearing reproduction Viking clothes. Introduce the idea of evidence-supported information by looking at real artefacts on a visit to a site, or see websites such as www.jorvik-viking-centre.co.uk.

> **Vocabulary:** *raid, raider, longboat, voyage.*

Life in a longhouse (page 28) helps the children make inferences about the Viking way of life from archaeological and picture evidence. The items are: 1) cauldron for cooking, 2) barrel for grain, 3) loom for weaving cloth, 4) bucket for collecting water, 5) fire for warmth and cooking, 6) chest for storage of valuables and clothes, 7) carved bed for the chief, father or mother, 8) wooden bowls for food. Discuss what it might be like to use these items instead of modern versions. Ask the children to consider to what extent the Vikings were like us. Were they like the Anglo-Saxon people? Did things change when they came and settled?

> **Vocabulary:** *longhouse, cauldron, loom.*

Viking evidence (page 29) highlights that, towards the end of the Viking period, between about 980 and 1066, many of the Vikings that were settlers rather than invaders were integrating with the Anglo-Saxons. They were trading rather than plundering, and some had adopted Christian customs and traditions. Monasteries were still being looted for their treasure – mostly chests full of coins and gold ornaments – and Viking beliefs and burial traditions were still strong. But in and around the Viking town of Jorvik, for example, Viking coins were being struck, grave plaques were being carved with images from sagas, and crosses were erected along waysides. The Vikings were skilful craftspeople, and these artefacts show that. The children can see photographs of such artefacts on the websites www.visitcumbria.com/wc/chc1.htm and www.bbc.co.uk/history/ancient/vikings/money_01.shtml.

> **Vocabulary:** *artefacts, plaque, carvings, Christian, pagan.*

King Alfred the Great: 1 and **2** (pages 30–31) introduces King Alfred and the impact he had on Britain. Tell the story of King Alfred using the activity sheet and if possible watch a DVD or video portraying his life, such as *Alfred the Great – King of the Anglo-Saxons* by the History Makers. Locate the boundaries of the Danelaw on a map of the UK. Split the class into groups and ask the children to rewrite a section of the story in their own words and illustrate it to make into class books. Encourage each group to read their book to the class. Ask them which are the most exciting parts of the story and why. Discuss why they think King Alfred is known as Alfred the Great and who called him that. Link this with work in citizenship (Children's rights – human rights).

> **Vocabulary:** *King Alfred, Christianity, treaty, partition, translation, settlement, Danelaw, biographer, pagan.*

Viking settlement (page 32) helps the children understand that accounts of Viking raids are Anglo-Saxon interpretations of the events. It is important that the children are able to assess the impact of an invading force. Study the class timeline and a map of Britain with all the areas of Viking settlement marked. Ask: how do we know the Vikings landed in these places? When did the Vikings first land here? How long were they here? Did they settle in our area? Which parts of Britain were not invaded by them? Help the children to draw conclusions about the extent and inferred impact through class discussion. Look at extracts from the Anglo-Saxon Chronicles (see www.bbc.co.uk/history/ancient/anglo_saxons/) that show the ruling and educated Anglo-Saxon view. Make sure the children know that most people were illiterate and the reports were interpretations. Help them form an opinion based on reports of killings and burnings of villages; but point out that many Vikings married local women. Encourage the children to find out more about the Anglo-Saxons, then work as a class to make a two-column comparative list of Anglo-Saxon and Viking life.

> **Vocabulary:** *invaders, settlement, raiders, Anglo-Saxon Chronicles, evidence, impact.*

Why did Henry VIII marry six times?

Henry VIII's wives (page 33) examines the different reasons for Henry's six marriages. Ask the children to suggest their own reasons why Henry VIII married six times, e.g. falling in love, wanting an heir, money, power, need for alliances. Together, list the reasons in order of importance. Suggest that the children produce a Tudor family tree on a large sheet of paper, highlighting Henry VIII's marriages and his children. They could draw or print pictures from the Internet to illustrate their family trees. Encourage them to add dates. This activity could be sensitively linked with issues in citizenship (How do rules and laws affect me?).

> **Vocabulary:** *marriages, wives, divorced, beheaded, betrayal, alliances, power, religion, Catholic, Protestant.*

The king's portrait (page 34) involves using a portrait as a source to find out about the appearance and character of Henry VIII. You could use portraits from the National Portrait Gallery website, www.npg.org.uk and from www.englishhistory.net/tudor/monarchs/henry8.html. These portraits are primary source evidence of fashions, wealth and behaviour because they are posed and show what the sitter wants. Consequently they may not be a true likeness. Consider why portraits were painted and whether poor people could afford to have them done. You could show the children portraits of Henry at different ages and together identify a list of similarities (same person, richly dressed, looking straight at you, broad shoulders, beard) and differences (clothes, age of person, colour of beard, weight changes). Use these to help the children understand what cannot be recorded in a picture: voice, behaviour, movement, personality, and skills and achievements.

> **Vocabulary:** *portrait, artist, record, appearance, personality.*

In **What Henry did** (page 35) the children learn about the power and importance of a Tudor king, and identify what monarchs did and did not do. To prepare for the activity you could organise the children into groups and ask them to find out what Henry did as a king. Set a time limit and ask them to make lists of his activities. Draw out that Henry was thoroughly engaged in state business, met with ambassadors, negotiated treaties, studied theology and was the first monarch to rule the Nobility of England and later the Church, but as a monarch he enjoyed his hobbies and wanted to be seen pleasing himself as evidence of his power.

> **Vocabulary:** *jousting, hawking, court, ambassador.*

Henry VIII's family (page 36) reinforces the reasons for Henry's marriages. Remind the children that Henry needed a male heir, money, power and influence in Europe. Explain that all three of Henry's legitimate children became monarchs after him and carried on the Tudor name. The children will need to refer to pictures of Henry and his children for the extension activity. You could tell the story of each queen using portraits on www.npg.org.uk and asking the children to act key scenes with you. Discuss the important issues sensitively: divorce, arranged marriage, infant death, adultery, execution. You can explain some of these in terms of children's friendships: disloyalty of a best friend, excluding someone from play, and the death of pets. This links with work in literacy (Drama) and citizenship (Children's rights – human rights).

> **Vocabulary:** *marriage, divorce, death, heir, beheaded, execution, unfaithful, allies.*

King Henry's reign (page 37) encourages the children to recall knowledge of Henry's character and consider different points of view. First bring together everything the children know about Henry in a class discussion. Ask the children to explain why he acted as he did and what happened as a result. They need to know his desperation for a male heir to continue the dynasty, which resulted in a social and religious upheaval, the break with Rome and the Catholic Church, and the establishment of a powerful monarchy ruling Parliament, the nobility and the country. Link this with work in citizenship on rights and responsibilities (Children's rights – human rights).

> **Vocabulary:** *religion, Church of England, divorce, heir.*

What were the differences between the lives of rich and poor people in Tudor times?

A Tudor house (page 38) helps the children make inferences about the lifestyles of different types of Tudor people by identifying features of Tudor buildings. A visit would be invaluable; alternatively take a photo tour of Tudor buildings on www.english-heritage.org.uk/education, www.hrp.org.uk or www.shakespeare.org.uk for palaces, castles, inns, farmhouses, churches, merchants' houses, doctors' houses and schools. Spot common architectural features: thatch, half-timbering, stone and brick decorations, sculptured chimneys, leaded windows, mullions. Discuss the wealth of people living in these buildings (90% of people lived in homes that have not survived, many of them hovels). Encourage the children to consider how comfortable the buildings would be, and to find out how the inhabitants heated and lit their homes.

> **Vocabulary:** *feature, wealthy, merchant, half-timbering, leaded windows, sculpture, thatch.*

Tools for the job (page 39) helps children learn about the types of evidence and gaps in the evidence about the poor of this period. Collect books about town and country and show the class how to research; provide key words to help the search (looking at both rich and poor to contrast): *country, cattle, sheep, wool, food, jobs, enclosures, villages, agriculture.* Set a time limit and give the children sticky notes to mark the books and paper for brief notes. They can make charts with two columns: *What I found out/What I would like to know.* Then use new key words to find answers. Contemporary paintings are evidence of wealthy people's concept of country life: the rich shown at their pastimes and the working poor shown colourful and content. Contemporary documents can show otherwise. Evidence of poor and working people's jobs is found in their tools, which were owned by the rich and often listed in inventories. You could photocopy pictures of artefacts for the children to guess their use.

> **Vocabulary:** *plough, loom, shears, gauntlet, wool.*

Tudor inventory (page 40) focuses on using inventories to make inferences about people's lifestyles. Inventories are lists of personal and household goods and monies, debts and sometimes instructions about bequests. In Tudor times every small item was valuable and so listed. Money was reckoned in pounds, shillings and pence (l.s.d.). Read extracts together from inventories, to help decipher Tudor spelling and syntax. See www.dur.ac.uk/4schools/Inventories/Source3.htm for examples. Discuss what these tell us about the owner: do many servants' beds mean the person actually has servants (or did have) and is wealthy? If they have much silver plate and cash, is this wealth? If someone has many animals, is he/she a farmer or do they need land as well? The poor did not have inventories at all; discuss possible reasons. The children can write an inventory listing their own most precious things. Link this with work in maths (Solving problems; Handling data).

> **Vocabulary:** *will, inventory, bequeath, gift, inherit.*

Rich and poor (page 41) encourages the children to consider the differences between rich and poor Tudors. Enlarge the picture on an overhead projector or interactive whiteboard and make inferences about the lives of the poor. Clues to the poverty of the pictured family include many things in one room, no separate kitchen and living area, bare floor, wooden stools instead of chairs and wooden rafters instead of a ceiling. Discuss the problems there might be in trying to find out about the poor in Tudor times, the types of evidence and the gaps in the evidence. Ask them to develop their answers on the sheet into a piece of extended writing. This activity can be linked to work in literacy (Creating and shaping texts) and citizenship (Living in a diverse world).

Accused (page 42) focuses on the attitudes of wealthier people towards the poor. The wealthy wool trade, enclosures, destruction of almsgiving monasteries, plague and war all resulted in massive poverty for a third of the population. Almshouses, workhouses and laws compelling monetary aid helped a little but the contrasts in wealth were stark. As a class, you could make a chart about the reasons for poverty and its effects. See www.spartacus.schoolnet.co.uk for extracts from contemporary writing about poverty and the law. You could link this activity with discussions in citizenship about the work of charitable organisations today.

Vocabulary: *law, punishment, workhouses, almshouses, peasant, plague.*

At the theatre (page 43) helps draw conclusions about life in Tudor times from the works of William Shakespeare and the theatres in which his plays were acted. If possible, arrange a visit to the reconstructed Globe Theatre, which is close to the site of the original theatre. There is much evidence of Tudor culture in Shakespeare's portrayals of everyday life, the royal family and historic events of the time. From the websites listed and from website www.angband.demon.co.uk/Globe/ the children can find out about mummers' plays and travelling players (acrobats, jugglers, musicians). Watch 'suitable' extracts from the DVD of the film *Shakespeare in Love* (cert. 15) to see what the Globe Theatre looked like in action and to see one of the famous Tudor plays. The plays were written with a mixed audience in mind so there was something for the rich and for poorer taste, each play having the antics of 'rude mechanicals' as well as courtly love.

Vocabulary: *theatre, plays, actors, jugglers, courtly.*

A journey by road (page 44) is a game which informs the children about travel in Tudor times. Explain that people travelled on foot, by horse (riding or driven) or by water (river or sea) and goods went by all three methods too. Collect books and use www.nationalgallery.org.uk for contemporary paintings to find examples of people travelling. Discuss who would travel for pleasure and who for work. Who would travel by horse? What were the implications – did it need food and shelter? Could you go further? Could a horse transport goods or power a plough? Make a class chart together to collate findings and about different methods of transport and who used them. Explain that most people stayed in their birthplace, except the destitute, who fled to towns. But tradesmen, politicians, intellectuals and the rich travelled across Europe and to the Far East.

Vocabulary: *merchant, blacksmith, stage wagon, barge, pillion.*

Exploring the world (page 45) helps the children to draw conclusions about life in Tudor times. They can find more information on website www.channel4.com/history/microsites/H/history/guide16/part12.html. For the extension activity the children's leaflets can include pictures and information about the places the explorers visited, their ships, and lists of the things they brought back. With the class, discuss the job of a navigator. Show the children compasses and allow time for them to use and experiment with them. Talk about what sort of experiences the sailors would have had on board a Tudor ship. Was it a dangerous voyage for both rich and poor? Explain how the sailors made maps as they travelled. You could show them the first atlas of Europe at www.bl.uk/onlinegallery/ttp/ttpbooks.html. In small groups the children can role-play explorers sailing to and discovering new lands. This supports literacy (Group discussion and interaction; Drama).

Vocabulary: *explorer, navigation, sailor, warship.*

What was it like for children in the Second World War?

The Second World War (page 46) introduces key information about the causes of the Second World War. Discuss when the war took place and the main countries involved. Mark on a timeline when the war started and finished, and add some of the key events. Explain that the Treaty of Versailles was an agreement that Germany was forced to sign after the First World War. It stated that Germany must pay for the damage done during the war and was not allowed to have a big army, tanks, submarines and warplanes. Germany became very poor, so its people turned to Adolf Hitler, leader of the Nazi party, because they believed he would make Germany a better place to live. With the class, visit a local war memorial. Ask when it might have been built. Explain that local war memorials usually list the names of soldiers killed in the First and Second World Wars. Encourage the children to record information by sketching and making tallies of names.

Vocabulary: *Nazis, Adolf Hitler, Germany, Poland, Treaty of Versailles, invade, defend, attack, war memorial.*

The Blitz (page 47) examines some of the characteristic features of the Blitz. Tell the children about the mass bombing of cities. Encourage them to suggest reasons why some areas of a city were more likely to be bombed than others. Explain that the bombing raids aimed to stop the manufacture of weapons and frighten civilians so that the government would surrender. Show pictures of bomb damage and newspaper accounts of the results of air raids. Find out if anywhere near you suffered bomb damage. You could read extracts from first-hand accounts at: www.bbc.co.uk/ww2peopleswar. Discuss what could be done to stop the bombers: anti-aircraft fire, blackouts, etc. Good fictional accounts to read to the class are *War Boy* by Michael Foreman and *Lizzy's War* by Elizabeth Beresford. This activity meets the requirements of literacy (Listening and responding).

Vocabulary: *air raid, the Blitz, anti-aircraft fire, blackout, bombers, bomb damage.*

Protection (page 48) looks at some of the initiatives the government introduced to protect people in Britain during the war. Discuss the different types of shelter available. Explain that they were very cramped and had no toilet or heating. The only light would be a torch or candle. Talk about the importance of the blackout and how people could be fined if they did not comply; lights could be used as targets to show the enemy where to drop bombs. After a few weeks of the Blitz, public shelters were provided with heat, lights and toilets, but it was difficult to sleep here as people would spend their time playing games, singing, dancing and talking. Introduce the idea of evacuation. Explain that Britain was divided into three areas: evacuation areas, reception areas and neutral areas. Find out which of the three areas the school was in. People would have to carry their gas masks everywhere, even in the country.

Special gas masks were made for babies. More information can be found at websites www.homesweethomefront.co.uk and www.britainatwar.co.uk. This activity can be used to support work in literacy (Group discussion and interaction).

> **Vocabulary:** *Anderson shelter, public shelter, gas mask, blackout, evacuation, advantage, disadvantage.*

Evacuees (page 49) can be used for display purposes. Encourage the children to describe some likely feelings of an evacuee and to use words associated with evacuation accurately and appropriately. Read extracts from eyewitness accounts. There are some good examples on the following website: www.bbc.co.uk/history/ww2children/home.shtml. If possible, link with an older class within the school and have them reply as parents to the letters your class has written. *Goodnight Mister Tom* by Michelle Magorian contains a useful fictional account of life as an evacuee. It may also be possible to get someone to come into school to talk about their experiences of evacuation. This activity links to literacy (Creating and shaping texts).

> **Vocabulary:** *evacuate, evacuees, billeting officer, host family, the Blitz, air raid, blackout, sirens.*

Wartime cakes (page 50) provides an opportunity to explore and taste the kind of food that was available during the war. Discuss with the children the foods that were in short supply, such as bacon, sugar and butter. Explain that rationing was introduced to share the little food there was fairly. Food rationing began on 8 January 1940. Everybody was issued with a ration book which they had to take to the shops with them. Provide descriptions of typical meals and ask the children to compare these with what they eat today. People would have had treats like cakes only on special occasions. Clothes were also rationed and people were issued with clothing coupons or would recycle old clothes. Discuss other things that could be recycled. Make a list. Tell the class that everyone was encouraged to grow their own food. Try growing seeds such as radishes with the class. These activities could be linked to work in Design and technology (Packaging) and Science (Helping plants grow well).

> **Vocabulary:** *rationing, ration book, reconstituted, powdered egg, supplies.*

Feelings and experiences (page 51) encourages the children to make deductions about the way people felt about how the war affected them. Before the children do the activity you could arrange for someone who was a child during the war to visit the class. Encourage the children to ask questions. Record the interview. Replay the tape and discuss with the children what they have learned about the history of the local area during the war, and how the visitor felt about his or her experiences. Help them to identify on a map local places mentioned by the visitor. Mark the map with a description of what happened during the war years. The children could role-play the characters on the activity sheet and carry out interviews in role. This activity meets the requirements of literacy (Drama).

> **Vocabulary:** *rationing, coupons, evacuation, host family, billeting officer, auxiliary fireman, home guard.*

VE Day (page 52) enables the children to communicate their understanding of the end of the war. Look at newspaper cuttings about VE Day. The children may like to hold their own street party celebrations in the playground with wartime food and music. Discuss with the children areas of conflict in the world today. Tell them about the United Nations and their role in peacekeeping. Discuss whether there is peace in the world today and whether things are better today than they were at the time of the Second World War. Information about conflicts today and their effects on children can be obtained from charities such as Christian Aid and the Red Cross. You could arrange for someone from one of these charities to come in and talk to the children and organise a fundraising event to collect money to help them in their endeavours. This work could be linked to citizenship (People who help us).

> **Vocabulary:** *celebrations, VE Day, street party, Churchill.*

What can we find out about ancient Egypt from what has survived?

Detective work (page 53) encourages the children to make inferences and deductions from ancient Egyptian artefacts. First find the ancient Egyptian period on a class timeline and show the geographical location on a map or globe. Explain how deciphering the Rosetta Stone in 1799 unlocked written evidence about this highly literate society. Tell the children that the discovery of Tutankhamun's tomb in 1922 provided further technological and cultural evidence. Look at pictures of the Valley of the Kings and discuss the desert burial site. Ask: why did the ancient Egyptians bury their royalty there? Where were poorer people and slaves buried? How did we know to look in the Valley of the Kings? Are photographs a good record? Mummified bodies found in the tombs have provided evidence of health, diet, religion and appearance. For more information, see www.britishmuseum.org and key in 'mummies'. Link to citizenship (Living in a diverse world).

> **Vocabulary:** *tomb, grave, sarcophagus, Rosetta Stone, Tutankhamun.*

The red and black lands (page 54) focuses on making deductions about life in the past from pictures of the landscape. Discuss what children already know about Egypt and help generate questions about the lives of the people. You could use Google Earth to look at the location and spot landmarks like the River Nile, the desert, Giza, etc. Can the children spot modern manmade features? Use websites such as www.corbis.com to view photographs of the landscape and remains like the pyramids, green and fertile riverside fields, temples, the arid Valley of the Kings. This activity could be linked to geography (Investigating rivers).

> **Vocabulary:** *River Nile, desert, fertile, flood plain.*

All kinds of people (page 55) helps the children make inferences and deductions from objects and pictures. Research evidence of clothes at www.museum.manchester.ac.uk and www.corbis.com. Look at tomb murals, relief sculptures, portraits on body coffins, jewellery, fabric and footwear. The children can make detailed drawings of clothing and equipment from photographs or from original sources in a museum. Add captions or labels to explain about the origin, the wearer, materials, use and suitability for life in that climate. Link with science skills in planning an investigation and in recognising a fair and an unfair test. Try experiments with cotton, linen and wool, to see which is coolest, which dries quickest and find out the source of each fabric. This supports work in science (Characteristics of materials).

> **Vocabulary:** *slave, pharaoh, priest, tunic, waistcloth, headdress, fabric, linen, cotton, jewellery.*

Ancient Egyptian objects: 1 and **2** (pages 56–57) provides illustrations of a range of objects the children can study and explore in more detail. Ask them to make a list of different types of evidence, discussing classifications like household, decoration, transport, foods and treasure. Discuss the decorations and link to work in art and design on colour, pattern, texture, shape, form and space. Produce illustrated charts to sort and classify finds according to material used, whether decorative, practical or protective, whether special skills were needed to make them (like jewellery or armour), or who used them and for what purpose. Provide time and resources for the children to find out more about the objects. Discuss what they found out and why these objects survived. Do we know more about rich or poor people? Why? The British Museum website www.ancientegypt.co.uk provides useful information and resources. This activity meets the requirements of literacy (Group discussion and interaction).

> **Vocabulary:** *senet board, canopic jars, sarcophagus, amphora, wood, pottery, stone, metal, ivory.*

Food and farming (page 58) explores a specific aspect of ancient Egyptian life. Encourage the children to make inferences and deductions about food and farming by looking at objects and pictures. Explain that what we know about the past is dependent on what has survived. Tomb murals show aspects of livestock and arable farming, irrigation canals, wine production, fruit growing, flocks of domestic geese, the spotted, horned cattle and hunting and fishing on the Nile. Crates of mummified beef were found in Tutankhamun's tomb. See the 'Voices from Ancient Egypt Gallery' at www.bbc.co.uk/history/ancient/egyptians/ for a transcript and audio presentation of a farmer's letters to his sons. Discuss the weather conditions needed for crops to grow. Explain that irrigation canals from the Nile were vital. This activity can be linked to work in science (Helping plants grow well).

> **Vocabulary:** *arable, livestock, rear, hunt, irrigation, canal, evidence.*

What has survived? (page 59) allows the children to investigate for themselves an aspect of ancient Egypt that interests them. Discuss with the children what they have learned about ancient Egypt. Provide time for the children to show their understanding of the characteristic features of Egyptian society at the end by encouraging the class to ask probing questions about their posters. This activity could be extended by using reference books and the Internet to see if they can find out more about their chosen objects. If desired the children could produce a final piece of written work to support their posters. This activity supports literacy (Group discussion and interaction; Creating and shaping texts).

> **Vocabulary:** *evidence, source, survive.*

What was it like to live here in the past?

Old or new: 1 and **2** (pages 60–61) can be used as a basis for an introductory discussion about how buildings are used and who uses them. You could take photographs of buildings in the local area and use them with the pictures on the activity sheet. Ask the children to arrange the pictures and photographs into a timeline and justify the reasons for their choices. Point out that many old buildings have been modernised. Take the children to visit local buildings and if possible provide evidence of what they looked like in the past from old photos and newspaper clippings. This work can be linked to geography (Investigating our local area).

> **Vocabulary:** *Tudor, Georgian, Norman, Victorian, modern, old-fashioned.*

Looking at maps (page 62) explores how an area has changed. The maps on the activity sheet concentrate on Euston in London. Enhance them by looking at the area on the Internet. Good maps are available at the following websites: www.oldlondonmaps.com/horwoodpages/horwoodmain.html, and www.streetmap.co.uk. The activity could be adapted for a study of your local area or as an introduction to looking at maps and recognising symbols, before looking at the local area around the school. If you have taken photographs of buildings in the local area, put them in the correct places on a large local map. When comparing the maps, the children should record their findings in a table using headings such as roads, railways, open spaces, amenities. The activity meets the requirements for core learning in geography (Investigating our local area) and literacy (Group discussion and interaction).

> **Vocabulary:** *maps, buildings, features, local, Ordnance Survey, area.*

Looking for clues (page 63) encourages the children to make deductions from physical evidence and recognise that some questions can be answered by looking at buildings whilst others cannot. Investigate the picture of the school on the activity sheet and compare to the children's own school. If their school is very similar to the one shown on the activity sheet, try to arrange a visit to another local but more modern school so that they can compare the features etc. Use documents and evidence from the past to help the children find out more. Encourage the children to write an accurate description of the building. This activity could be extended to link with citizenship (Respect for property).

> **Vocabulary:** *school, playground, entrance, exit, materials, evidence, documents.*

School log book (page 64) provides an example of a written source that gives information about the areas where people live. Other school records include admission registers and punishment and attendance records. Show children examples of these records from their own school and point out that these are primary sources. Other good examples of school log books can be found at: www.berksfhs.org.uk/journal/Mar2003/HiddenTreasuresIn SchoolLogBooks.htm and www.scan.org.uk/researchrtools/school logbook.htm. This activity can be used to support work in literacy (Understanding and interpreting texts).

> **Vocabulary:** *written evidence, log book, primary source.*

Moving

Relate one's own experience to the concept of settlement

- **Read the interviewer's questions.**
- **Write your replies.**

1. Do you know anyone who has moved?

2. Why did they move?

3. Would you like to move? Give your reasons.

4. Why do you think people move house?

Now try this!

- **Write about where you would like to live when you grow up.**
- **Give your reasons.**

Teachers' note Ask the children to name anyone among their relatives and friends that has moved home or country – immediate family members, neighbours or unconnected new people moving into an empty house. Discuss reasons for moving away from or into an area: starting a new job, need for a job, to be near school, to a larger home, to join family, to make a new life away from trouble.

Developing History
Ages 7–8
© A & C BLACK

Coming to Britain

Recognise that people have always moved between different areas

- **Find out about an ancient people who came to Britain. Fill in the boxes.**

Name of people _____

When did they come?

Where did they come from?

Why did they come?

How did they travel?

What did they do?

Where did they settle?

Now try this!

- **Write how we know about these people.**
- **With a partner, discuss the things you think they took with them on their journey.**

Teachers' note The children will need access to books, CD-ROMs and/or the Internet for research. Suggest websites such as www.bbc.co.uk/history/forkids. Before photocopying, fill in the name of the invaders or settlers you are studying. Remind the children that some reasons for people in history moving to Britain were the same as those of people alive today. Encourage them to talk about their own experiences or those of their family, and the idea of settlement.

Developing History
Ages 7–8
© A & C BLACK

Invaders and settlers: 1

Learn who invaded and settled in Britain a long time ago

Key

	Anglo-Saxons
	Normans
	Romans
	Vikings

BALTIC SEA

NORTH SEA

BLACK SEA

ADRIATIC SEA

ATLANTIC OCEAN

MEDITERRANEAN SEA

N
E
S
W

Teachers' note Enlarge this map by photocopying onto an A3 sheet or on an interactive whiteboard and use with page 15. Mark your school's hometown before copying. Ensure the children can recognise land/sea differences on the map, and that they colour in and follow the key properly. The children can also use the map to show the area of the empires or territories of each group of invaders and settlers.

Developing History
Ages 7–8
© A & C BLACK

Invaders and settlers: 2

Learn who invaded and settled in Britain a long time ago

- **On the map, colour the countries the Vikings came from.**
- **Colour the key to match.**
- **Label the countries.**
- **Draw an arrow to show their journey to Britain.**
- **Now do the same for the other peoples.**

Word bank

England	Italy
France	Norway
Germany	Scotland
Iceland	Sweden
Ireland	Wales

Use an atlas to help you label the countries.

Romans 55 BC–AD 406

Vikings AD 793–1066

Normans AD 1066–1485

Anglo-Saxons AD 406–1066

- **Cut out the cards.**
- **Sort them into the correct order.**

Teachers' note The children can work in pairs or groups. They will need coloured pencils in four different colours and access to atlases, books, CD-ROMs and the Internet for research. Explain that they should choose a different colour for each group of invaders or settlers. They can mount the cards on an A3 sheet of paper to make a timeline, and add more information and dates to it.

Developing History
Ages 7–8
© **A & C BLACK**

Take a good look

Find out what can, and cannot, be learned from archaeological remains

- **Work with a partner. Your teacher will give you an** artefact .
- **Look at it carefully and make notes.**

What size and shape is it?	How is it decorated?
What is it made from?	Where was it found?
How old is it?	What was it used for?

I think it is a _____.

Now try this!

- **Draw the object carefully.**
- **Label as many details as you can.**

Teachers' note Provide a suitable artefact for the children to examine. Ideally the children should be able to handle or touch the artefact at a site or museum, or you may be able to loan an item from your local authority. Alternatively, use good-quality A4 photographs. Encourage the children to make a 'best guess' about what the object is and what it was used for. This should be followed up with further research from other sources.

Developing History
Ages 7–8
© **A & C BLACK**

People of Britain and Rome

Comparing the lifestyles of Celts and Romans

- **Look at how these people are dressed.**
- **Write the similarities and differences.**

Celts

Romans

Similarities	Differences
<u>Children are dressed like the adults.</u>	<u>The Roman man is wearing a toga.</u>

Now try this!

What do the people's clothes tell you about where they live and their lifestyles?

- **Talk to a partner about your ideas.**

Teachers' note Explain that the Celts were the people who lived in Britain before the Romans arrived, and locate the Celtic and Roman periods on a timeline. Encourage the children to compare the style of Celt garments, accessories, gender differences and what materials were used. Back this up with original evidence from research (jewellery, pictures, artefacts). Discuss wealth, style and decoration. Which style was more decorative? Were patterns and shapes different?

Developing History
Ages 7–8
© A & C BLACK

A Roman soldier's pack

To select and record information about the Roman way of life

A Roman legionary carried a heavy pack on campaigns.

- **Label the things on the pack.**
- **Find out what each one was used for.**
- **Complete the boxes.**

Word bank
rolled up cloak
carrying pole
leather bottle
mattock
pot and pan
turf cutter
leather satchel

pot and pan
Used for boiling water and cooking.

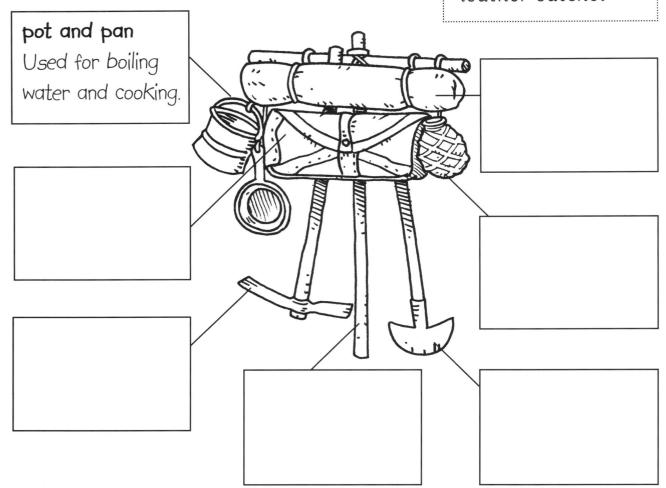

Now try this!

- **Find out what equipment Celtic warriors carried.**
- **What was it used for? Make notes.**

Teachers' note Explain the term 'campaign'. Ask the children to guess what a tool could do – 'This looks like it can cut things'. They may have had camping experiences using modern equivalents. Discuss why each legionary would need these things on a long journey and how the pack was carried. The soldiers carrying the packs were known as Marius's Mules, after their famous general of that name and the pack animal.

Developing History
Ages 7–8
© A & C BLACK

Latin phrasebook

- **Cut out the cards.**
- **Match the Latin words with their English meanings.**
- **Glue the pairs onto paper.**

Use a dictionary to help you.

Latin words	English words
mille	queen
canem	moon
luna	king
annus	dog
cave	thousand
rex	beware
exit	year
regina	he goes out

- **Write what you think this Latin sign means.**

CAVE CANEM

_____

Now try this!

- **Make a list of places and objects where you might see Latin words today.**

Teachers' note The children will need access to dictionaries. Discuss the Latin language used by the Romans and how many Latin words are still in the English language. Show examples of Roman buildings or artefacts with Latin inscriptions on them. The children could use books to find out about Roman numerals then write some numbers that are important to them, like their age, house number and the year they were born. The sign means 'Beware of dog'.

Developing History
Ages 7–8
© A & C BLACK

19

Boudicca's revolt

Learn the main events in, and reasons for, Boudicca's revolt

This cartoon strip tells the story of Boudicca's fight against the Romans.

• **Write a caption for each picture.**

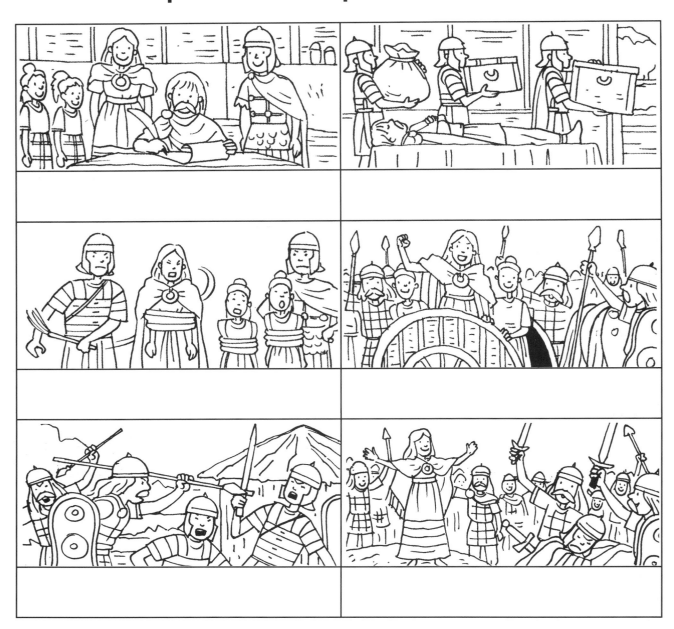

Now try this!

• **Imagine you are Boudicca, planning to attack the Romans.**
• **Write your battle plans.**

Teachers' note Discuss Boudicca's revolt and its causes. Put across the idea of treachery, anger and revenge, and that many Romans felt that Celts' goods were fair plunder. Write key words on the board to help with captioning the story. Make sure children understand that there are different interpretations of the revolt and that sources contradict each other. Remind them that many Celts and Romans co-existed peacefully in other parts of the country.

Developing History
Ages 7–8
© A & C BLACK

Visit to a Roman town

To compare Roman and Celtic lifestyles

- **Imagine you are a Celt visiting a relative in a Roman town in Britain.**

- **Write a list of what you see and experience.**

I can see ...	I can hear ...
men wearing togas	

| I can smell ... | I can taste ... |

| I can visit ... | I can buy ... |

Now try this!

- **Describe your visit to a partner.**

- **Explain how the town is different from a Celtic town.**

Teachers' note Use this sheet to help the children summarise or get an overview of their studies of Roman Britain. Ideally, take the children to visit a Roman site or museum of Roman artefacts before doing this activity. The children can work in pairs or groups. Discuss with them what life was like in a Roman settlement in Britain, both from the Celts' and Romans' points of view. They can look at books, CD-ROMs or the Internet to help them.

Developing History
Ages 7–8
© A & C BLACK

Jumbled up Anglo-Saxons

Recognise characteristics that place Anglo-Saxons as having lived long ago

- ## Cut out the captions and picture cards.
- ## Match the correct heads, bodies and legs to make the four people. Then add the captions.

| rich woman | working man | rich boy | poor girl |

- ## Imagine you are one of the rich people.
- ## Write how you get dressed in the morning.

Teachers' note The children should cut out the cards and stick them onto A4 or A3 sheets then label them as much as they can. Discuss social status, gender and age shown by the clothes. The children can draw in extra items of jewellery and weapons, and colour in the drawings.

Developing History
Ages 7–8
© A & C BLACK

Skilful Anglo-Saxons

Learn about the way of life of the Anglo-Saxons

The **Anglo-Saxons** used lots of 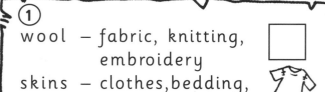 natural resources .

- **Match the resources to their products and uses.**
- **Write the correct letter.**

Resources

A oxen
B wild birds
C fish
D fruit and nut trees
E sheep
F iron ore
G large trees
H wild animals

①
wool – fabric, knitting, embroidery
skins – clothes, bedding, leather
meat – food
horn – spoons, handles, combs
bone – spoons, tools
fat – soap, candles
☐

②
flesh – food
bones – needles, glue
☐

③
meat – food
skins – clothes, bedding, leather
antlers – handles
bone – tools
☐

④
wood – furniture, resin, houses, ships, fuel
☐

⑤
meat – food
skins – clothes, bedding, leather
horn – cups, war horns
power – ploughing, pulling carts
☐

⑥
meat – food
feathers – arrow flights, pillows, pens
☐
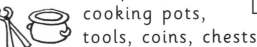

⑦
wood – furniture, chests, charcoal, handles
food – fruits, nuts
☐

⑧
iron – weapons, cooking pots, tools, coins, chests
☐

Now try this!

- **List some other natural resources and how the Anglo-Saxons used them.**

Teachers' note Discuss the concept of natural resources and how the Anglo-Saxons 'lived off the land'. Children will need to have had a little experience of Saxon artefacts and skills beforehand. The evidence of such artefacts needs a leap of imagination: although we can be fairly certain we are correct to infer that a needle would have been used to sew with, we don't know if this was cloth or the skin of a wound. Answers are: 1E, 2C, 3H, 4G, 5A, 6B, 7D and 8F.

Developing History
Ages 7–8
© **A & C BLACK**

23

The ship burial at Sutton Hoo

Learn about Sutton Hoo and make inferences about archaeological evidence

- **Look carefully at the pictures.**
- **Describe the treasures.**

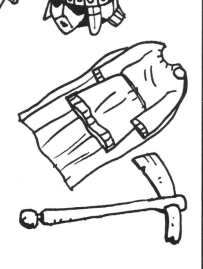

musical instruments	
weapons	
clothes	
accessories	a belt accessory
other items	

Now try this!

There was no body found at the site.

- **Write what you think the treasures tell you about the person who owned them.**

Teacher's note Explain that Sutton Hoo is an archaeological site in Suffolk, which was excavated in 1939. The activity sheet shows rare and valuable treasures that were found buried there in a huge ship grave. Discuss the children's favourite possessions. Then discuss the items pictured. How many are richly decorated and rare? Prompt them to ask further questions. Why was the burial in a ship? Was this person a sailor?

Developing History
Ages 7–8
© A & C BLACK

Anglo-Saxon health quiz

Make connections between information provided by many sources

- **Read the statements.**
- **Circle true (T) or false (F).**

		T	F
1.	Anglo-Saxons had toilets with running water.	T	F
2.	They got drinking water from rivers and wells.	T	F
3.	Historians have found evidence of herbs as medicines.	T	F
4.	Sometimes wells were near cesspits and toilets.	T	F
5.	Anglo-Saxons had regular warm baths.	T	F
6.	They got illnesses with indigestion and diarrhoea.	T	F
7.	They had regular dental check-ups.	T	F
8.	Rubbish was collected by the council each week.	T	F
9.	Bones from Anglo-Saxon times have been found with sword wounds, breaks, amputations and arthritis.	T	F
10.	Many combs of the time have been found with head lice in them.	T	F

Your score ___ /10

Now try this!

Do you think the Anglo-Saxons were healthy?

- **List your reasons.**

Work with a partner.

Teachers' note The children will need access to a range of sources for research: books, CD-ROMs and the Internet. They can attempt this individually or in pairs. Mark it as a class so that you can have a show of hands for each question. Children who have the right answer can explain their decision, citing any evidence they have. This way you can discuss the reasons they give for an answer. The answers are: 1F, 2T, 3T, 4T, 5F, 6T, 7F, 8F, 9T and 10T.

Developing History
Ages 7–8
© A & C BLACK

The Battle of Hastings

Discuss ideas associated with settlement and invasion

- The ⌐Bayeux Tapestry⌐ records the battle in pictures.
- Describe what is happening in each scene.

- Discuss with your group how the Anglo-Saxons might have felt when the Normans invaded.

Teachers' note The children should work in groups to talk about the pictures. They depict: 1 – King Edward the Confessor with William of Normandy and Harold, earl of Wessex, who fought for the English throne after his death; 2 – The Normans building boats to invade England; 3 – The Normans sailing to England; 4 – Anglo-Saxon soldiers; 5 – Norman horsemen charging; 6 – Harold being shot by an arrow in the eye.

**Developing History
Ages 7–8
© A & C BLACK**

Viking raiders

Find out about Viking longboats and make inferences about the Viking way of life

- **Imagine you are a Viking** [raider].
- **Underline the items you would take on a raid to Britain.**

To help you decide:
- think what the things were used for
- there would not be much room in the longboats
- the voyage might be dangerous
- the voyage may take days or weeks.

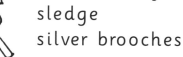

fur cloaks
wooden barrels
gold and silver coins
knives, all sizes
pottery bowls
wooden bowls
iron helmet
iron cauldron
Thor's hammer amulet
wooden bed

drinking water
sheep
chain mail
spare sails
loom
woollen thread
wheat and barley
new timber for a roof
sledge
silver brooches

- **Write five more things you would take.**

- **Discuss which three things were the most important to take.**
- **Give your reasons.**

Now try this!

Work in a group.

Teachers' note The children will need access to books, pictures and websites about Vikings and their ships. Help them identify categories such as weapons, food, treasure, clothes, ship-mending and making equipment. Discuss why some things are essential: weapons for protection at sea and on raids; fishing equipment for the voyage; clothes for warmth. Missing items are the longboat and its equipment (oars, anchor), shields, swords and food for the journey.

Developing History
Ages 7–8
© A & C BLACK

Life in a longhouse

Make inferences about the Viking way of life

- **Look at this picture of a Viking** longhouse .
- **Complete the key.**

Key

☐	barrel
☐	bed (carved)
☐	bucket
☐	cauldron
☐	chest
☐	fire
3	loom
☐	wooden food bowl

- **Write what each item was used for.**

1. _____

2. _____

3. _____

4. _____

5. _____

6. _____

7. _____

8. _____

- **Draw the outside of a longhouse and label it. Use a picture or photograph to help you.**

Teachers' note Discuss the one-room layout of the Viking longhouse and compare with the children's homes. Remind them that this picture is a reconstruction based on different sources. Point out that some longhouses were thatched. For the extension activity the children will need access to pictures of the exterior of Viking longhouses.

**Developing History
Ages 7–8**
© A & C BLACK

28

Viking evidence

Ask and answer questions from archaeological and picture evidence

- **Look at these Viking** artefacts **. Complete the chart.**

	grave plaque	cross (part of)	coins	chest
What was it made of and why?	Stone. So it was not damaged by the weather.			
Where and how was it used?				
What does it show?			A King's head	
Where might you see it today?				

- **What do the carvings and images show about Viking customs and beliefs?**
- **Give your reasons.**

Now try this!

Teachers' note Enlarge this sheet by photocopying onto A3 paper so children can see the details of the images. Introduce the activity by explaining that we can use artefacts to find out about the everyday life of people in the past. Discuss why stone and metal are used for things that are to be used outdoors or handled a lot. Remind the children that the Vikings were invaders then settlers, and how Christianity influenced their pagan traditions and beliefs. The Vikings used carvings on important items, so the cross, coins and plaque may have been for a chief.

Developing History
Ages 7–8
© A & C BLACK

King Alfred the Great: 1

Recall, select and organise knowledge about King Alfred

- **Read the story of King Alfred.**

Alfred became King of Wessex at the age of 21 in 871.

The Danes, led by King Guthrum, forced King Alfred's army to withdraw into Somerset.

In Somerset, King Alfred was sheltered by a peasant woman. While thinking how to regain his kingdom, he burnt the cakes he had been asked to watch.

Alfred disguised himself as a minstrel to sneak into Guthrum's camp. There he discovered Guthrum's plans.

Because of what he had discovered, Alfred decided to fight the Danes.

In May 878, Alfred's army defeated the Danes, at the Battle of Edington.

Alfred negotiated peace with the Treaty of Wedmore. King Guthrum and his army agreed to convert to Christianity.

In 886, Alfred made a partition treaty with the Danes. East England became ruled by the Danes and known as 'Danelaw'.

Alfred organised a building programme of well-defended settlements across southern England, to stop the Danes breaking the partition treaty.

To ensure lasting peace, Alfred arranged the translation from Latin to Anglo-Saxon of books he felt were important.

Teachers' note Use this with the activity on page 31. Read the story of King Alfred. Make sure the children understand all the vocabulary. Cut the story into strips and mix them up. In pairs, encourage the children to try to organise the story back into the right order. What clues did they use to help them?

Developing History
Ages 7–8
© A & C BLACK

King Alfred the Great: 2

Recall, select and organise knowledge about King Alfred

Alfred's ┃biographer┃, Bishop Asser, said:

Alfred attacked the whole pagan army fighting ferociously in dense order, and by divine will won the victory, made great slaughter among them and pursued them to their fortress ... After 14 days, the pagans were brought to extreme depths of despair by hunger, cold and fear, and they sought peace.

Which battle do you think Bishop Asser was talking about and when was it fought?

_____

_____

- **Choose a part of King Alfred's life. Write about it as if you were his biographer.**

 • **Why is this king known as Alfred the Great?**

Teachers' note Use this with page 30. After the children have familiarised themselves with the main aspects of the story, read the quote from Bishop Asser. Discuss what a biographer is and why they are important to historians. Encourage the children to write about King Alfred's life in their own words. Suggest they decorate the first letter as the Saxons would have done. Allow time to compare their stories.

Developing History
Ages 7–8
© A & C BLACK

Viking settlement

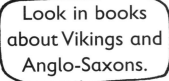

- **Imagine you are an Anglo-Saxon in Britain.**
- **Write about the Viking invaders.**

> Look in books about Vikings and Anglo-Saxons.

> Find a map of Viking times showing the Danelaw.

> Look at old documents such as the Anglo-Saxon Chronicles.

> Visit the BBC history website.

When the raiders came I felt _____

_____

After they had gone we _____

_____

Before they came we were _____

_____

When they were here we _____

_____

I think the Vikings _____

_____

Now try this!

- **List reasons why the Vikings came to Britain. Did they take anything back to their homeland?**

Teachers' note Provide resources so that the children can find out about the Vikings and Anglo-Saxons. Discuss the Anglo-Saxons' reactions and feelings and write some of the children's suggestions on the board. Guide the discussion using examples from previous studies to show that the initial impact was one of destruction and violence. However, their lifestyles were similar, and in time mixed communities were formed.

Developing History
Ages 7–8
© **A & C BLACK**

Henry VIII's wives

Learn and remember the names and order of King Henry VIII's wives

- ## Cut out the cards about Henry VIII's wives.
- ## Match the information to the correct wife.

 **Catherine of Aragon**	Henry had this wife beheaded in 1536. She also gave him a daughter, Elizabeth.
 **Anne Boleyn**	This wife outlived Henry. She looked after him through sickness and old age, until he died in 1547.
 **Jane Seymour**	Unlike the previous wife, this wife was beautiful but the marriage lasted only two years. She was beheaded for betrayal.
 **Anne of Cleves**	Henry married this wife ten days after Anne's beheading. In 1537 she gave birth to Edward, but she died two weeks after the birth.
 **Catherine Howard**	Henry agreed to marry this wife after seeing a picture of her, but divorced her after a few months as she looked nothing like her portrait.
 **Catherine Parr**	She gave birth to a daughter called Mary. They were married a long time but Henry divorced her in 1533 because he wanted a son.

Teachers' note Explain that the portraits, but not the texts, are in the correct order. Read the information with the children and ensure they understand what each card says. After they have completed the activity sheet, suggest they try turning them face down and playing pairs with a partner.

Developing History
Ages 7–8
© A & C BLACK

The king's portrait

Ask and answer questions using a portrait as a source

- **Look carefully at a portrait of Henry VIII.**
- **Describe what you can see.**

The portrait was painted by _____.

The date of the portrait is _____.

Henry was _____ years old.

Word bank

dignified common proud modest stiff relaxed fierce shy
peaceful aggressive calm bold strong weak old young
unfriendly friendly exciting boring clever stupid fat thin
handsome ugly rich poor powerful weak large small

King Henry VIII looks _____

_____

_____

_____

_____

Now try this!

Do you think Henry VIII would have been happy with this portrait?
- **Write your reasons.**

Work with a partner.

Teachers' note Provide a portrait of Henry VIII on the interactive whiteboard or in a book for children to study carefully. Find out the date it was painted and help the children work out Henry's age. Encourage the children to use their own vocabulary as well as that suggested. Discuss reasons he was painted like this – to look commanding, rich, powerful, attractive, stronger than others, someone his subjects could admire.

Developing History
Ages 7–8
© A & C BLACK

What Henry did

- **Find out about the jobs and activities Henry did.**
- **Cut out the pictures and heading cards.**
- **Put the pictures under the correct heading.**

Use books, CD-ROMs and the Internet.

What King Henry did		What King Henry did not do	
hawking	ploughing	thatching	cooking
cutting wood	dancing	fighting	reading
washing	going to church	hunting	guarding palace
playing music	jousting	signing official papers	sewing

Now try this!

Which of the king's activities would you like to do?

- **Write about it and give your reasons.**

Teachers' note Use books and the Internet to find pictures of Windsor Castle or Hampton Court to show the children. They can work in pairs with these to discuss what they think Henry would have done there. The children will need access to books, pictures and websites about Henry VIII and Tudor times. They could mount the two sets of cards side-by-side on an A4 sheet.

Developing History
Ages 7–8
© A & C BLACK

Henry VIII's family

Learn about the reasons for and the results of Henry's marriages

• Complete the crossword.

Clues across
1 Henry's first wife was Queen _____. (9 letters)
2 He got a _____ from her and people were angry. (7 letters)
3 His daughter from Anne Boleyn was Queen _____. (9 letters)
4 Henry was the head of the House of _____. (5 letters)
5 Henry made himself head of the Church of _____. (7 letters)

Clues down
1 Henry married his fourth wife, Anne of Cleves, to make _____ in Europe. (6 letters)
2 Henry needed a son to be his _____ .(4 letters)
3 Catherine's daughter, _____ , later became queen. (4 letters)
4 Henry's third wife, Jane Seymour, gave him a son called _____. (6 letters)
5 Two wives were unfaithful and he had them _____. (8 letters)
6 The family name of Henry's fifth wife was _____. (6 letters)

Word bank
ALLIES
BEHEADED
CATHERINE
DIVORCE
EDWARD
ELIZABETH
ENGLAND
HEIR
HOWARD
MARY
TUDOR

Use capital letters.

• Imagine you are a Tudor artist.
• Draw a picture of Henry and his children.

Teachers' note Explain how to do a crossword and discuss how most of the answers show the reasons for and results of Henry's marriages. Point out that the clues are mostly but not all in chronological order. Remind the children of the meaning of 'allies' with reference to modern-day allies such as Britain and the United States.

Developing History
Ages 7–8
© A & C BLACK

King Henry's reign

Extract information from descriptions about the character of Henry VIII

- ## Read what two historians said about Henry VIII.

Henry was a good king that all the people loved. His strong army and navy kept England safe from invaders and there was no war. He said the Church took money from the poor. So he took the treasures and land from the Churches and England became rich and merry. He set up a new Church of England so that the people didn't have to do what the Pope in Rome said. Henry said that prayers should be in English not Latin, so that the ordinary people could join in. He made himself head of the new Church so that he could get a divorce at last. He needed a new, younger wife to give him a son to rule after him. Queen Catherine was too old to be his queen. He wanted to make sure his family were England's kings in the future. He finally got his only son, Edward VI.

Henry was always a bully who wanted all the power and got his own way in everything. He was one of the worst kings. He made the ordinary people pay more taxes to keep his Court rich and merry. He took the treasures and land from the churches and monasteries so people had no work there. He made a new Church of England with himself as the head. This meant he ruled the country and the Church and he could get a divorce from Queen Catherine. None of her sons lived and he needed a son to carry on the Tudor name. He married six times to try and get sons but had only one, the sickly Edward, who died young. He made war on France and Scotland and wasted the country's money. The people were poor from paying high taxes and having their land used for sheep.

- ## Discuss these passages with a friend.
- ## Underline in blue the parts you do not agree with.
- ## Underline in red the parts you think were most important to Henry.

Now try this!

- ## Which of these passages do you think is most truthful and why?

Write on the other side of the sheet.

Teachers' note Display the sheet on an interactive whiteboard and read the passages aloud, then discuss each one separately. Help the children identify what they agree with – Does this make sense? Have you found this out in your work? They can underline part of a sentence. Help them recall evidence to support what they say. They can use books and their own work to check facts.

Developing History Ages 7–8
© A & C BLACK

A Tudor house

In Tudor times, some people became wealthy and built houses with new features.

- Complete the labels on this merchant's house. Describe how each feature made houses better than before.

Work with a partner.

| Brick chimneys | Tiled roof | Leaded glass windows |

| Stone entrance extension | | Up to three storeys high |

| Painted half-brick and timber walls | Stone floor — Flat slabs of stone. Stopped dampness rising up. |

Now try this!

- **Imagine you were a servant working in this house.**
- **Write about the jobs you did.**

Teachers' note Make sure the children have seen pictures of a variety of Tudor houses. You could scan this picture onto an interactive whiteboard and discuss what materials are Tused. Encourage the children to discuss which features on the illustration they have in their own homes, what their functions are and what materials are used today.

Developing History
Ages 7–8
© A & C BLACK

Tools for the job

Learn about the lives of the poor in Tudor times from a variety of evidence

- **Match these Tudor workers with their tools.**
- **Describe what each tool was used for.**

A mill-stone

Used to grind corn into flour.

_____

B gauntlet

_____
_____
_____

C shears

_____
_____
_____

D wooden tub

_____
_____
_____

E wood plane

_____
_____
_____
_____

F plough

_____
_____
_____

A

G wooden pail

_____
_____
_____
_____

H loom

_____
_____
_____
_____

- **List the jobs you would like to do.**
- **Give your reasons.**

Teachers' note Discuss Tudor country life, explaining that most people worked on the land. There were no machines to help them. Look at these artefacts and ask the children to think of modern equivalents and to match the job title with the tool, for example shearer and shears. Add a hint that the wool trade was booming. Washerwoman using a wooden tub to wash clothes and hawker using a gauntlet to protect his hand can be found by elimination.

Developing History
Ages 7–8
© A & C BLACK

Tudor inventory

Use inventories to draw conclusions about life in Tudor times

• **Read this** inventory **of a Tudor inn.**

<u>The parlour above the hall</u>
One long table, one forme, one chare, one little round
table, a little open cubard 6s 8d
Two standing beddes, a trindell bed furnished with
bedding and bolster 40s
A little iron chimnay, a bason and ane ewer,
 2 puter candlesticks, 3 quysshons 7s
<u>The little chamber</u>
2 beddes, furnished for men servants, ane old chaire,
a little table 10s
<u>The loft benethe the doores</u>
Two beddes furnished for women servants 10s

Part of innkeeper Christopher Dale's inventory, 1570

'Parlour' comes from
the French word
parler meaning 'to
speak'. It was partly
a room for sitting
and talking in.

Who used the parlour and what for? _____

_____

_____

Why were the candlesticks important? _____

_____

What do you think the basin and ewer were used for?

_____

How do you think Christopher Dale's bed differed from his
servants' beds? _____

_____

Now try this!

• **Draw some of the furniture in the inn.
Use pictures of Tudor furniture to help you.**

Teachers' note Read the list aloud for the children to follow. Ask them to spot items that are unfamiliar and discuss
possible explanations – bason and ewer (basin and pewter jug), trindell bed (one that pulls out from under main bed),
cubard (cupboard), chare (chair). Explain about counting money in pounds, shillings and pence. Work out with the
children how much the things in these rooms total (£3 13s 8d) and compare with today's prices.

**Developing History
Ages 7–8
© A & C BLACK**

Rich and poor

Learn about the wealthy and poor in Tudor times

- **Look at this picture of a Tudor family at home.**
- **Answer the questions.**

Does the picture show a rich or poor family?

_____

What evidence can you see in the picture to support this?

_____

_____

_____

_____

What was bad about being poor in Tudor times?

_____

_____

What was good about being rich in Tudor times?

_____

_____

- **Would you have preferred to live as a rich or a poor person in Tudor times?**
- **Give your reasons.**

Teachers' note The children will need some prior knowledge of how rich people lived in Tudor times. Ask the children to list things in the picture that identify the family as rich or poor. Compare this to what they found out about the inn from the inventory on page 40. How are the people's lives different? What do they think the children in the picture will do when they grow up? Do they have good prospects?

Developing History
Ages 7–8
© A & C BLACK

Accused

Learn about the attitudes of wealthier people towards the poor

- **With a partner, talk about what these wealthy Tudor people thought about poor people.**

- **Write a sentence about each person's view. Did they agree?**

The landowners enclose all the land into pastures for sheep … the peasants must depart away … what else can they do but steal or go about begging?

Written by King Henry VIII's adviser Sir Thomas More in 1516.

They are punished by whipping. Yet they like this life so much that their punishment is soon forgotten.

Written by Elizabethan author Thomas Harman in 1566.

_____

_____

_____

_____

_____

_____

A poor boy is accused of stealing a loaf of bread.

- **Write what he might say.**

I am 8 years old. I live on the streets.

I only stole because …

- **Find out how he might have been punished by law.**

Now try this!

Do you think Tudor punishment was too harsh?

- **Write your view and give your reasons.**

Teachers' note Read the extracts aloud and discuss what they show about the attitudes of the writers. Help children understand that there were many causes of poverty in Tudor times. There was a system of law and order to control and severely punish the criminal poor but also ways to help the deserving poor. The children will need access to suitable resources to research law and order in Tudor times.

Developing History
Ages 7–8
© A & C BLACK

At the theatre

Draw conclusions about life in Tudor times from different sources

- **Find out about the Globe Theatre.**
- **Fill in the report.**

You could look at these websites:
www.william-shakespeare.info
www.bardweb.net/globe.html

Where was the theatre?

_____

What happened here?

_____

Who came to watch?

_____

Did they sit or stand to watch?

_____

Who were the actors?

_____

Who wrote the plays?

_____

What was the building made from?

_____

What happened to the first Globe Theatre?

_____

_____

Now try this!

- **Write a Tudor person's diary page about a night at the Globe Theatre.**

Teachers' note The children will need access to the Internet or other resources about the Globe Theatre. Remind them how to make brief notes to record information. Explain that the Globe Theatre Tudor was originally built in Elizabethan times. The theatre that exists today is a modern version that opened in 1997. For the extension activity, remind the children that a diary is written in the first person.

Developing History
Ages 7–8
© A & C BLACK

A journey by road

Make inferences about the lives of the rich and poor in Tudor times

- **Tudor** [merchants] **travelled to cities by horse. The journey was always eventful.**
- **Play the game with a partner and discuss the events.**

1 Begin your journey to the city by horse.	**2** You meet other travellers and journey together.	**3** Your horse loses a shoe. Stop at the blacksmith. **Miss a turn.**	**4** Deep ruts in the road. **Go back 2 squares.**	**5** You make a night-time stop at an inn. **Miss a turn.**
10 A stage wagon passes by, pulled by 10 horses.	**9** It rains all day and the road becomes waterlogged. **Go back 1 square.**	**8** Your companions change direction. You go on alone.	**7** You meet a cart, tie your horse behind it and hitch a ride. **Move on 3 squares.**	**6** After a rest, your horse goes quickly. **Move on 2 squares.**
11 A troop of soldiers gallops past. You get covered in mud. **Go back 1 square.**	**12** You pass a carriage with a broken wheel and stop to help. **Miss a turn.**	**13** You spend the night in a barn. **Miss a turn.**	**14** To get medicine for your horse, you stop at a monastery. **Miss a turn.**	**15** You cross a river bridge. **Move on 1 square.**
20 You meet a dung cart, which is very smelly. **Miss a turn.**	**19** Along a river bank, you see the King's barge.	**18** You reach a ford flooded by heavy rain. **Miss 2 turns.**	**17** You stop to give food to a poor family. **Go back 1 square.**	**16** You see a poor family ahead, travelling on foot.
21 A woman riding pillion on a horse falls off. You stop to help. **Miss a turn.**	**22** You stay the night at a farm to rest your horse. **Go back 3 squares.**	**23** A beggar stops you on the road. **Miss a turn.**	**24** The King's messenger rides past.	**25** You stop at an inn for some food and to rest your horse. **Go back 1 square.**
30 You ride into the city.	**29** You get caught in a thunderstorm. **Miss a turn.**	**28** The royal procession rides past.	**27** City watchmen arrest the robbers and return your horse. **Move on 1 square.**	**26** A gang of robbers steals your money and horse. **Go back 2 squares.**

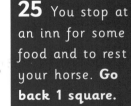

Teachers' note The children should play in pairs. Enlarge the game onto an A3 sheet. Discuss how wealthy and poor people travelled in Tudor times, and set the journey in the context of the countryside of the time. Explain that most roads were in poor conditions, and there were lots of pitfalls along the way. The children will need a dice and counters to play the game. They should take turns to roll the dice and move their counter.

Developing History Ages 7–8
© A & C BLACK

Exploring the world

- ## Cut out the cards about Tudor explorers.
- ## Sort the cards into these groups: | fact | and | opinion | .

Tudor explorers brought back new foods to Britain.

Sir Francis Drake was the greatest explorer who ever lived.

Sailors in Tudor times all behaved like pirates.

The biggest danger that sailors faced was attack by sea monsters.

Navigation in Tudor times was complicated.

The Mary Rose was King Henry VIII's favourite warship.

Life on board ship was very cramped, but fun.

Sir Walter Raleigh discovered the potato.

Now try this!

- ## Work with a partner.
- ## Find out about a Tudor explorer and make a leaflet about his life.

Teachers' note Discuss the difference between fact and opinion. The children should work in pairs and explain their thinking as they sort the cards. Encourage them to say whether they agree with the opinions. They could use books, CD-ROMs and the Internet to check that the facts are true and find out more information. Tell the children the names of Tudor explorers, such as John Cabot, John Hawkins, Martin Frobisher, Walter Raleigh, Francis Drake and Richard Chancellor.

Developing History
Ages 7–8
© **A & C BLACK**

The Second World War

Describe reasons and results

- **Cut out the cards.**
- **Match each** `fact` **to the correct** `reason`.

Facts	Reasons
The Germans were unhappy after the First World War (1914–1918) …	… because they wanted to make Germany rich and powerful again.
The Nazis started to invade other countries …	… because they had promised to defend Poland if it was attacked.
The Second World War began on 1 September 1939 …	… because Germany had been building up its armies and weapons since 1933.
Britain declared war on Germany on 3 September 1939 …	… because they were made to sign the Treaty of Versailles.
For the first year of the war Britain and France were not strong enough to stop Hitler …	… because Germany invaded Poland.

- **Why was it called a World War?**
- **List the countries that took part.**

Teachers' note Read the facts and reasons to the children. Working in pairs, the children should cut out the cards and match each fact with the correct reason. During the plenary, ask them to explain how they worked out which belonged together. Use maps to establish why it was a world war.

Developing History
Ages 7–8
© A & C BLACK

The Blitz

Use terms about the passing of time

What would it have been like before, during and after an air raid?

- Imagine you were there.
  Make notes on the chart.

	Before	During	After
I can see …			
I can hear …			
I can smell …			

Teachers' note Look at the picture with the class and discuss what is happening. Ask the children to use their senses to describe what is happening. Tell them that 'the Blitz' is the term used for the German air raids on Britain in 1940–1. Explain that the Germans bombed London because that is where the government is located. At one stage London was bombed every day or night for three months. Manchester and Liverpool were also heavily bombed because of their industry (manufacture of ships and aeroplanes) and docks (where food was imported).

Developing History
Ages 7–8
© A & C BLACK

Protection

Discover how people were protected in the war

- ## Look at the ways families could protect themselves.
- ## Write an advantage and a disadvantage for each.

	Advantages	Disadvantages
Anderson shelter		
Public shelter		
Gas mask		
Blackout		
Evacuation		

Would you have wanted to be evacuated?
- ## Talk about your reasons with a partner.

Teachers' note Use the pictures to discuss ways families could protect themselves during the Blitz. Brainstorm the advantages and disadvantages of each method as a class before the children complete the activity sheet. Suggest why evacuation was used as one strategy to protect children. Encourage the children to give their own thoughts and views on evacuation.

Developing History
Ages 7–8
© A & C BLACK

Evacuees

Discover how people were protected in the war

- **Imagine you have been** evacuated **from a big city into the country.**
- **Write a letter home to your family.**

Word bank

air raid
billeting officer
blackout
the Blitz
host family
sirens

The Old Farm,
Frogholt,
Downshire
3 June 1940

_____

_____

_____

_____

_____

_____

Now try this!

- **Imagine you had stayed in the city.**
- **Write a letter to a friend who has been evacuated.**

Teachers' note Read extracts to the children from novels/stories about evacuation, as well as eyewitness reports (available on the Internet). Ask the children to imagine they were evacuees and to write a letter home. Ask them to consider why they might want to be evacuated and why not, what is happening to them and how they feel about it. Explain the words in the word bank and encourage the children to use the appropriate vocabulary.

Developing History
Ages 7–8
© A & C BLACK

Wartime cakes

Investigate what people ate during the war

• Try making cakes from this wartime recipe.

Ingredients

1 level tablespoon egg powder

2 tablespoons water

4 oz national (plain) flour

2 oz sugar

2 oz butter

½ level teaspoon baking powder

cake cases

Method

1. Mix the egg powder and water and allow to stand for five minutes. Work out any lumps with a wooden spoon and beat with a fork.

2. Cream the fat and sugar.

3. Add the reconstituted egg, flour and baking powder.

4. Mix well into a soft consistency.

5. Divide into cake cases. Makes approximately six small cakes.

6. Bake in a moderate oven for 30 minutes until golden brown.

Teachers' note Carry out this practical activity in small groups. First read the recipe with the children and ensure they understand the instructions. If possible, use old scales and weights. Talk about imperial measurements of weight and their metric equivalents. Most of these ingredients were rationed, so this recipe would be used on special occasions only. Discuss why certain foods were rationed.

Developing History
Ages 7–8
© A & C BLACK

Feelings and experiences

Communicate knowledge and understanding

- Imagine you asked these people how the war has affected them.
- Write their answers.

Now try this!

- **Find out about the Home Guard.**
- **Who were they? What did they do?**

Teachers' note Recap, through question and answer, what the children have learned so far about the war's impact on people of the time. List some of the effects of war on everyday life. Suggest ways in which people suffered. Discuss the pictures and brainstorm ideas of what the people may be saying. Encourage the children to consider the people's feelings. For the extension activity the children will need access to information sources.

Developing History
Ages 7–8
© A & C BLACK

51

VE Day

- **Write a newspaper report about the VE Day celebrations.**

The Daily Recorder

Wednesday 9 May 1945

The hard road to victory

How the war ended

_____
_____
_____
_____
_____

A huge street party

_____
_____
_____
_____

Churchill speaks

_____
_____
_____
_____
_____

Dancing in the street

_____
_____
_____
_____

- **Find out about the United Nations and how they helped keep the peace.**

Now try this!

Use books and the Internet to help you.

Teachers' note Show the children information and pictures of VE Day from books, newspaper cuttings and eyewitness accounts. Tell them that VE (Victory in Europe) Day was 8 May 1945 and point out the date of the newspaper on the activity sheet. Explain Churchill's role in broadcasting to the nation that the war had been won. Discuss the features of newspaper reports and the tense the children will use.

Developing History
Ages 7–8
© A & C BLACK

Detective work

- ## Look at this ancient Egyptian object.

Use books and the Internet to help you.

←————— 2 m —————→

- ## Fill in the report.

Size and shape:_____

What is it used for? _____

How old might it be? _____

Description of the decoration:_____

_____

Where would it have been found? _____

_____

How do we know what is inside? _____

_____

What does it tell you about Egyptian life? ___

_____

Now try this!

- ## Look closely at another Egyptian object used in a tomb. What does it tell you about the people who made it?

Teachers' note Enlarge and project the image of the sarcophagus on an interactive whiteboard. Ask the children to discuss archaeological digs and finds in Egypt, and ancient Egyptian customs and beliefs. Help them to find out about sarcophagi. Provide resources for the children to investigate pictures of other Egyptian artefacts.

Developing History
Ages 7–8
© A & C BLACK

The red and black lands

Make deductions about life in the past

This picture shows the River Nile in about 1500 BC.

The Egyptians called the deserts 'red lands' and the Nile floodplains 'black lands'.

- **What does the landscape tell you about what life might have been like in ancient Egypt?**

Things that made life easy	Things that made life difficult

Now try this!

Why was the River Nile so important?

- **Discuss with a friend.**

Look at Egypt and the Nile in an atlas to help you.

Teachers' note Explain that the Nile provided food, water and transport. In contrast the desert was used for burials, hence the pyramids. Discuss how in ancient times the Nile was a method of transport and provided water for crops. Discuss the annual flooding and how this improved fertility of the soil. Point out the boats and the canal. The children will need atlases for the extension activity.

Developing History
Ages 7–8
© A & C BLACK

All kinds of people

Make inferences about the way of life in ancient Egypt

- **Study these ancient Egyptians.**
- **Fill in the chart.**

Word bank

bodysock cape dress jewellery
lionskin tunic waistcloth wig

slave girl   pharaoh   rich lady   palace guard   priest

	What they are wearing	How I can tell their importance and what they did
slave girl		
pharaoh		
rich lady		
palace guard		
priest		

Now try this!

- **With a partner, talk about what the slaves thought of the Pharaoh.**
- **Explain why slaves were important in ancient Egyptian life.**

Teachers' note Answers: slave – dress; pharaoh – tunic, cape, jewellery; rich lady – bodysock, cape, jewellery, wig; guard – tunic, waistcloth; priest – tunic, lionskin. Ask how we know what Ancient Egyptians wore. Explain that information has been gathered from their tomb murals. List other forms of evidence. Discuss the structure of Egyptian society and how slaves and conscripts were used for large-scale projects. Do we know more about rich or poor people? Why?

**Developing History
Ages 7–8
© A & C BLACK**

Ancient Egyptian objects: 1

Classify information in various ways

pyramid

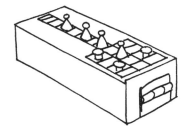

senet board

bowl

bed

chair

lamp

lute

wig

mirror

canopic jar

fan

sandals

Teachers' note Use this with page 57. Copy both sheets onto card. Children should work in small groups. Encourage the children to sort the cards multiple times, into categories such as types of materials, foods, clothes, houses and household items. Not every card will fit each category.

Developing History
Ages 7–8
© A & C BLACK

Ancient Egyptian objects: 2

Classify information in various ways

sarcophagus

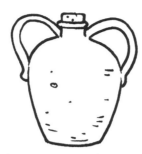

wine amphora

bow and arrows

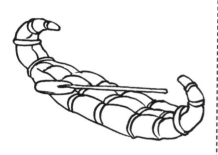

boat

statue of Ra

box for eye-paint

clappers

oven

harp

plough

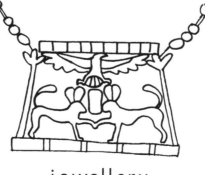

jewellery

nemes headcloth

Teachers' note Use this with page 56. Copy both sheets onto card. Children should work in small groups. Encourage the children come up with their own categories and ways of sorting the items. Talk about the reasons for their choices. Think of other items not here that could be added to each group.

Developing History
Ages 7–8
© A & C BLACK

Food and farming

Investigate a specific aspect of life in ancient Egypt

- **Tick the chart to show how the ancient Egyptians obtained these foods.**

Food	Grown	Reared	Hunted	Caught	Collected
grapes					
antelope					
goats					
honey					
fish					
dates					
eggs					
geese					
leeks					

- **In pairs, discuss how people in ancient Egypt got their food. How do you know?**

Think pictures, not words!

_____

_____

Now try this!

- **Find out how the Egyptians made wine, beer and bread.**
- **What evidence is there?**

Use books and the Internet to help you.

Teachers' note Explain that most ancient Egyptians were farmers who were dependent on the River Nile. Start by discussing how they obtained food by growing crops, raising animals, hunting, gathering and fishing. Talk about the objects and paintings that have survived that tell us this. Consider the evidence available that shows how they made wine, beer and bread. These are mostly wall paintings.

Developing History
Ages 7–8
© A & C BLACK

What has survived?

Find out about ancient Egypt from what has survived

- **Choose a topic about ancient Egypt to investigate.**
- **Find three pictures or objects that tell you about this topic.**
- **Complete the chart.**

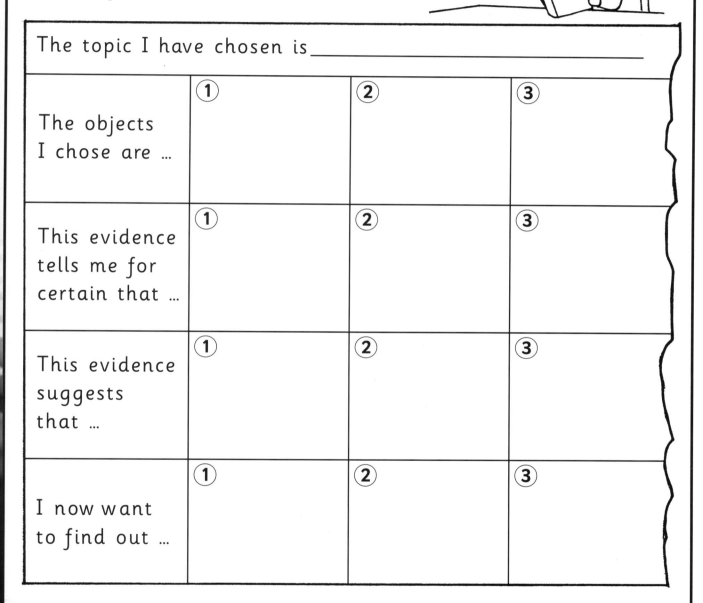

The topic I have chosen is _____			
	①	②	③
The objects I chose are …			
	①	②	③
This evidence tells me for certain that …			
	①	②	③
This evidence suggests that …			
	①	②	③
I now want to find out …			

 Now try this!

- **Make a poster to explain your findings to the class.**

Teachers' note The children could work individually, in small groups or in pairs. Before they start, discuss ideas for topics such as art, buildings, writing, technology, transport, clothes, beliefs, mummification, etc. Provide a selection of books and pictures for the children to choose three sources that support their topic. Discuss not only what is known but what is not known from what has survived.

Developing History
Ages 7–8
© A & C BLACK

Old or new: 1

Categorise buildings as old or new

- **Cut out the pictures.**
- **Sort them into** old **and** new .

Work with a partner.

Norman church

Victorian factory

supermarket

modern house

petrol station

Victorian school

Now try this!

- **Arrange the buildings in a timeline,** oldest **to** newest .

Teachers' note Use this activity sheet in conjunction with page 61. Use the illustrations to stimulate discussion about the different types of buildings. Discuss what is meant by 'old' and ensure the children recognise the buildings. Encourage the children to suggest similar buildings in their own locality. When they have finished, ask them to explain the reasons for their choices.

Developing History
Ages 7–8
© **A & C BLACK**

Old or new: 2

Categorise buildings as old or new

- **Label the pictures.**
- **Cut them out.**
- **Sort them into** old **and** new .

Word bank

petrol station	school
corner shop	Tudor house
Georgian terrace	church

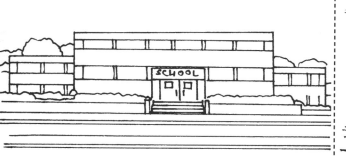

_____

_____

_____

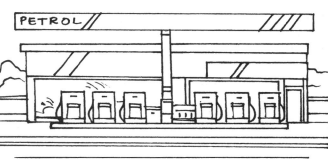

_____

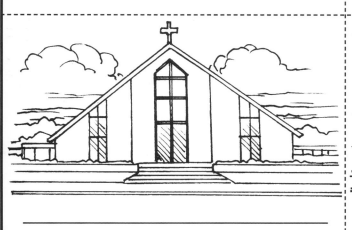

_____

_____

Teachers' note Use this activity sheet in conjunction with page 60. Ensure the children recognise all the buildings and compare them to similar buildings in the local area. Some of the buildings on this page have the same purpose as those on page 60, but are from a different period in time. Discuss the differences. The children can glue all the pictures in order on a large sheet of paper to make a timeline, and label features of the buildings.

Developing History
Ages 7–8
© **A & C BLACK**

Looking at maps

Compare how areas have changed over time

- Compare the features shown on these two maps.
What is the same? What has changed?

Euston in London in about 2000

The Polygon was a 15-sided building of 32 houses.

Euston in London in about 1800

Look carefully at the roads, buildings and place names.

- Make a chart to show what the changes are.

Now try this!

Teachers' note Enlarge the activity sheet onto A3 paper. Divide the children into small groups. Give each group an enlarged copy of the activity sheet. Use OHT acetates to outline some of the prominent landmarks from the old map. Discuss what is meant by 'features' – roads, buildings, open spaces. Compare this OHT with the present map. What buildings have appeared or disappeared? How has the area changed over the last 200 years? In their groups, encourage the children to devise their own table to record these changes.

Developing History
Ages 7–8
© A & C BLACK

Looking for clues

Find out about the past from looking at buildings

You can find out about the past by looking at old buildings. This building was built in about 1850.

• Look at the picture and answer the questions.

What was the building used for?

_____

What is it made of?

_____

_____

How might a similar building look today?

_____

_____

_____

Now try this!

• Write two questions you would like to ask to find out more about this building.

Teachers' note Tell the children that we know a lot about the past and local areas from buildings. Show them pictures of buildings near your school. Use similar questions to discuss what this shows about the local area. Look at size, number of rooms, decorative features and layout as clues to these local buildings' uses. Encourage the children to ask questions about the places even if they cannot be answered.

Developing History
Ages 7–8
© **A & C BLACK**

School log book

Recognise different written sources provide different information

These extracts come from a 1930s school log book.

Aug 1st 1934	*The timetable was not adhered to this afternoon – gardening being taken from 1.30 – 2.45 for the purpose of lifting the potato crop. During the lesson Arthur Howard stuck a garden fork through his foot into his toe. There was no question of fooling about in any way. This boy was actually digging & it was a pure accident. I asked the school Nurse to call & dress the boy's foot at his home 200 yards away to which he was immediately sent. The office was also notified.*
Nov 9th 1934	*The fireplace in Standards I & II Room is broken and the room gets filled with smoke. Wrote to the County Architect explaining & requisitioning repair, asking him to treat as a matter of urgency.*
Nov 14th 1934	*Children dismissed at 3.50 on account of darkness owing to a very thick fog. Walk home was dangerous, older children asked to pilot little ones. All children warned of road dangers before dismissal.*

Who do you think wrote the log book?

_____

What were the main topics recorded?

_____

_____

What does the log book tell you about the school and about the children who went there?

_____

_____

Now try this!

- **Choose an event in the log book.**
- **Imagine you were there.**
- **Write about what happened.**

Teachers' note For further information and entries in Camelsdale School's log book see: www.camelsdale.w-sussex.sch.uk/centenary_logbook.asp. During the plenary, discuss with the children what sort of information they have found out from the school log book and compare lifestyles then and now.

Developing History
Ages 7–8
© A & C BLACK